Back to Basics

ENGLISH

for 7-8 year olds

BOOK ONE

Sheila Lane and Marion Kemp

The alphabet

The capital letters are: A B C D E F G H I J K L M N O P Q R S T U V W X Y Z
The small letters are: a b c d e f g h i j k l m n o p q r s t u v w x y z

Fill in the missing capital and small letters.

A		D		G		J		M	N				S		V	W			Z
	b	c		e	f		h	i		k	l			o	p	q	r		t	u			x	y	

Write the letters again in the empty rings. Put them in **alphabetical order**. The first one is done for you to show you what to do.

1 (m) (k) (n) (l)   (k) (l) (m) (n)
2 (v) (x) (w) (u)   ( ) ( ) ( ) ( )
3 (r) (o) (q) (p)   ( ) ( ) ( ) ( )
4 (h) (f) (i) (g)   ( ) ( ) ( ) ( )
5 (e) (d) (b) (c)   ( ) ( ) ( ) ( )

Write each set of words in **alphabetical order**.
The first one is done for you.

1 bear   dog   ant   _ant_   _bear_   _dog_
2 leg   arm   toe   _____   _____   _____
3 hat   coat   shoe   _____   _____   _____
4 Tom   Carol   Janet   _____   _____   _____
5 zoo   sty   den   _____   _____   _____
6 cat   pig   dog   _____   _____   _____

Sets

Finish each sentence:

Janet's book is about

_____

Tom is reading about

_____

Read the names of these **sets** of things.

fruits	vegetables	trees
colours	clothes	insects

Here are 3 sets of pictures:

1
2
3

 Fill in the name of each set.

These are all _trees._____

These are all _____

These are all _____

Here are 3 more sets:

1
2
3

Write a sentence for each set.

These are all colours.

_____

_____

Here are 3 more sets:

Add more names to each one.

TOYS 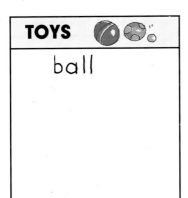	BIRDS	ANIMALS 
ball	robin	cat

Sentences

A **sentence** begins with a capital letter and ends with a full stop.

Can you read this sentence?

Jackandhismotherwerepoor.

Pull the words apart like this:

| Jack | and | his | mother | were | poor. |

Now read the sentence. Jack and his mother were poor.

Write these sentences with a space between each word:

1 Jacktooktheirlittlecowtomarket.

_____

2 Hesoldthecowforfivebeans.

_____

3 Jack'smotherwasveryangry.

_____

4 Shethrewthebeansoutofthewindow.

_____

Write the 4 sentences correctly.

the puppet ran away from his master once there was a wicked witch the king rode a beautiful white horse by morning the straw was spun into gold

_____

_____

_____

_____

_____

Spelling

Write the missing letters in the alphabet.

a _ _ _ e _ _ _ i _ _ _ _ _ o _ _ _ _ _ u _ _ _ _

Check your alphabet from page 2.

The letters **a e i o u** are called **vowels**.	The letters you have written in are called **consonants**.

Make words by putting in **vowels**.
Use different vowels in each set.

1 b _ g	**2** p _ t	**3** d _ g	**4** t _ p	**5** f _ n	**6** h _ t
b _ g	p _ t	d _ g	t _ p	f _ n	h _ t
b _ g	p _ t	d _ g	t _ p	f _ n	h _ t

Sometimes the letter **y** is used as a vowel.

Write the letter **y** to complete each word.

b _   c r _   m _   t r _   f l _   s t _   d r _   w h _

Use the words you have made to complete these sentences:

1 The _ _ _ flew _ _.   **2** Don't give up, just _ _ _.

3 The opposite of wet is _ _ _.   **4** Where's _ _ coat?

5 The pigs were in a _ _ _.   **6** _ _ _ did Pat _ _ _ ?

Understanding a story

The story of
<u>The Lion and the Mouse</u>
has been written without
capital letters or full
stops.
Can you read it in one
breath?

a mighty lion caught a tiny mouse in
its paw the lion agreed to let the little
mouse go free some time later the lion
was trapped in a net the mouse gnawed
away the ropes and set the lion free

 Write the story in 4 sentences.

_____

_____

_____

_____

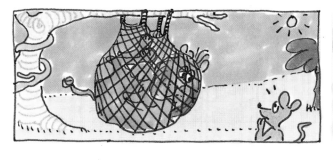

_____

_____

_____

_____

Write the missing words from the story.

1 The lion caught a mouse in its _____ .

2 The lion let the little mouse ____ _____ .

3 Later the lion was _____ in a _____ .

4 The _____ gnawed away at the _____ and

the _____ was set free.

Which is it?

 Write the missing vowels in the alphabet.

| _ | b | c | d | _ | f | g | h | _ | j | k | l | m | n | _ | p | q | r | s | t | _ | v | w | x | y | z |

Do you write **an** or **a**?

| Always write **an** before words beginning with vowels. | Always write **a** before words beginning with consonants. |

 Fill in each space with **an** or **a**.

_____ egg _____ hat _____ tree _____ umbrella _____ ball

_____ owl _____ arm _____ island _____ flower _____ man

_____ old hat _____ pretty picture _____ angry face

_____ new coat _____ ugly duckling _____ happy teacher

Do you write **to** or **two**?

 Fill in each space with **to** or **two**.

1 Ten and _____ make twelve.

2 Ahmet went _____ see Neil and Mary.

3 I walk _____ school with my friends.

4 At _____ o'clock I am going out _____ meet Karen.

5 My _____ best friends are coming _____ tea on Sunday.

Sentences

Read this muddled sentence: | went to the park children The

Read this sensible sentence: | The children went to the park.

Write each group of words in the right order to make a sensible sentence. Remember the full stop.

1 were playing rounders Diana and her friends

_____

2 playing football enjoys Robert

_____

3 Lucy to see her grandmother went

_____

4 and whales swim Sharks water in

_____

5 aeroplanes fly Birds in the air and

_____

6 in trees Most apes and live monkeys

_____

Puzzle corner

How many different sentences can you make from the **sentence machine**?

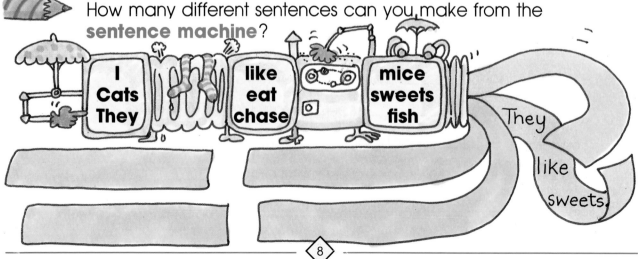

8

The alphabet

✏️ Fill in all the missing capital and small letters.

A _ _ _ _ _ _ H _ _ _ _ _ _ O _ _ _ _ _ _ _ _ _ _ Z

a _ _ _ _ _ _ _ _ _ k _ _ _ _ _ _ _ _ _ _ _ _ _ z

Check your alphabet from page 2.

✏️ Fill in the answers to these questions about the 26 letters of the alphabet:

1 The last letter of the alphabet is _____.

2 The fifth letter of the alphabet is _____.

3 The letter before w is _____.

4 The letter before m is _____.

5 The letters on each side of g are _____ and _____ .

These letters are in alphabetical order, but some have been left out.

✏️ Write the word which the missing letters spell.

1 k l _ n _ _ q   m o p

2 e _ g h _ j k l m _   _ _ _

3 r _ _ u v w x _ z   _ _ _

4 a _ c d _ f _ h   _ _ _

5 _ _ p q r s _ u   _ _ _

✏️ Add **one** straight line to make each shape into a capital letter like this:

⊢ Ε Ν _ <

Spelling

Say the sound of each of these consonants:

 Write the first letter of each word to make a new word.

1 <u>p</u>encil <u>i</u>nk <u>g</u>ate

___ ___ ___ = _____

2 ball elephant dog

___ ___ ___ = _____

3 mouse apple needle

___ ___ ___ = _____

4 cup orange tree

___ ___ ___ = _____

5 window elephant tree

___ ___ ___ = _____

6 snake umbrella needle

___ ___ ___ = _____

Say the sound of this consonant: **s**
Say the sound of this consonant: **h**

 Push the **two** sounds together to make **one** sound like this:

Complete each word with **sh**, **sp**, **st** or **sw**.

1 _ _ i d e r **2** _ _ i p **3** _ _ i c k **4** _ _ i m
5 f i _ _ **6** w a _ _ **7** b r u _ _ **8** n e _ _

 Complete each sentence with the right word.

1 I can _____ well. —— shell / spell

2 I like to eat _____ . —— sweets / sheets

3 _____ swim in the sea. —— Sparks / Sharks

4 Monkeys _____ in the trees. —— sting / swing

Sets

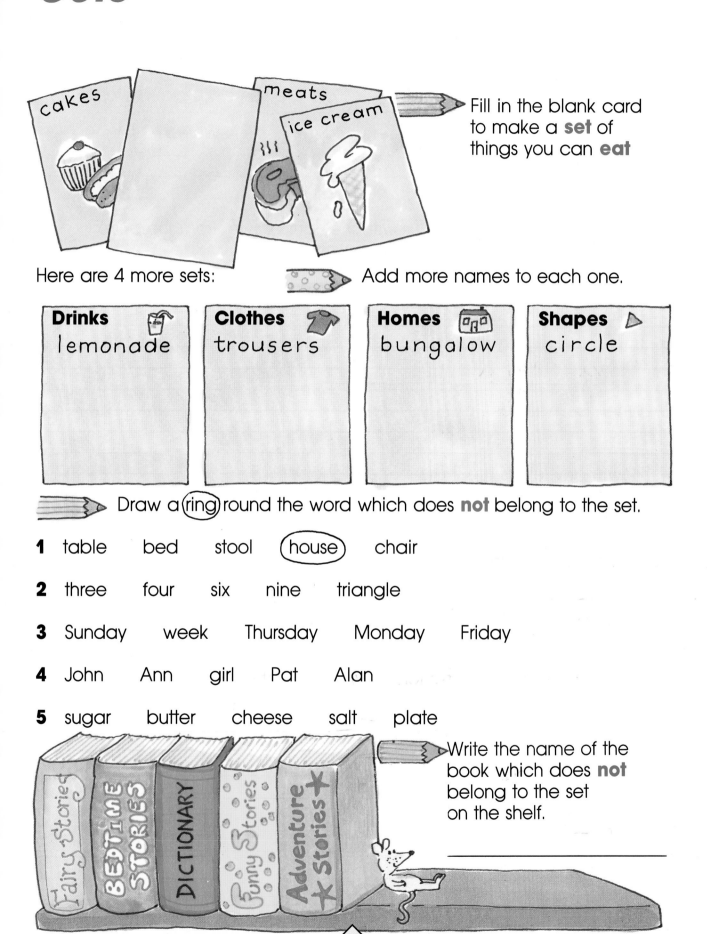

cakes

meats

ice cream

Fill in the blank card to make a **set** of things you can **eat**

Here are 4 more sets:

Add more names to each one.

Drinks
lemonade

Clothes
trousers

Homes
bungalow

Shapes
circle

Draw a ring round the word which does **not** belong to the set.

1 table   bed   stool   (house)   chair

2 three   four   six   nine   triangle

3 Sunday   week   Thursday   Monday   Friday

4 John   Ann   girl   Pat   Alan

5 sugar   butter   cheese   salt   plate

Write the name of the book which does **not** belong to the set on the shelf.

Fairy Stories   BEDTIME STORIES   DICTIONARY   Funny Stories   Adventure Stories

_____

Sentences

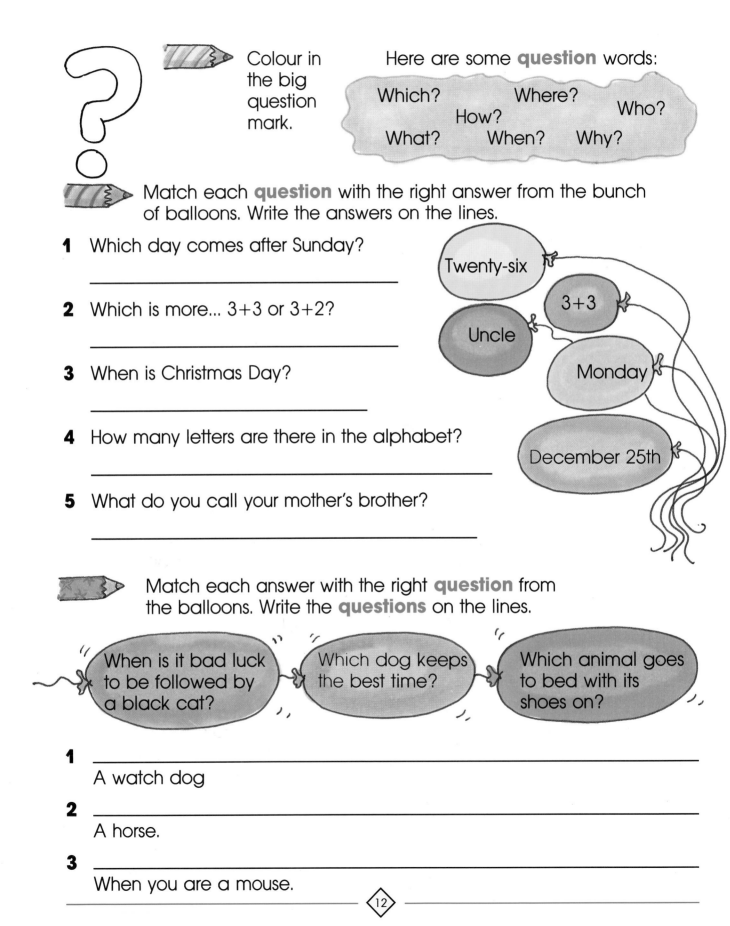

Colour in the big question mark.

Here are some **question** words:

Which?   Where?   Who?
How?
What?   When?   Why?

Match each **question** with the right answer from the bunch of balloons. Write the answers on the lines.

Twenty-six   3+3   Uncle   Monday   December 25th

1 Which day comes after Sunday?

_____

2 Which is more... 3+3 or 3+2?

_____

3 When is Christmas Day?

_____

4 How many letters are there in the alphabet?

_____

5 What do you call your mother's brother?

_____

Match each answer with the right **question** from the balloons. Write the **questions** on the lines.

When is it bad luck to be followed by a black cat?   Which dog keeps the best time?   Which animal goes to bed with its shoes on?

1 _____

A watch dog

2 _____

A horse.

3 _____

When you are a mouse.

Which book?

Read these questions: Which book would give you the answers? Write the **title** of the book each time.

1 Can all birds fly? _____

2 Which fish live in the sea? _____

3 Which farm animals lay eggs? _____

4 Do fish lay eggs? _____

5 What colour are robins' eggs? _____

Read the **contents** page of a book about farm animals. Write the number of the page where you could find out about:

CONTENTS	page
Hens and chickens	4
Animals which give milk	9
Caring for pigs	14
Sheep	20
Farm horses	26

1 Chickens ... page ▢

2 Lambs ... page ▢

3 Piglets ... page ▢

4 Calves ... page ▢

5 Foals ... page ▢

Puzzle corner

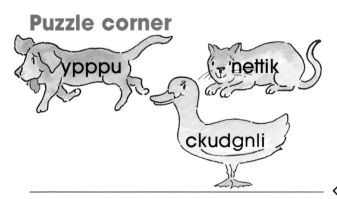

ypppu

'nettik

ckudgnli

 Write the names of the baby animals correctly.

_____

_____

_____

Naming words

Read this list of **naming words**:

 Tick the names of things which you can wear.

ball	doll	sandal
slipper	poppy	shoe
rose	jigsaw	lily

 Write the names from the box under the correct shop.

TOY SHOP   **FLOWER SHOP**   **SHOE SHOP**

_____   _____   _____

_____   _____   _____

_____   _____   _____

Naming words are called **nouns**

Read this list of **nouns**:

chimney	stairs	walls	tyres	horn	wheel
window	brake	door	wiper	gutter	knocker

 Write the **nouns** in the correct shape.

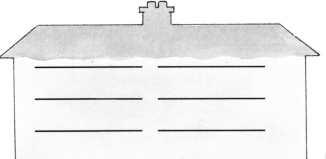

 Write each **noun** as a separate word.

appleinkeelowlumbrella

_____   _____   _____   _____

Sentences

What is in the Christmas stocking?   Write here:

a juicy —┐ of sweets
of slippers ┤ a pair
a pack ┘ orange
a book
of cards   a box
of puzzles

1 _a juicy orange_
2 _____
3 _____
4 _____
5 _____

Match the two parts of each sentence.

1 On Christmas Day   shines with fairy lights.

2 I can't wait   I wake up early.

3 Our Christmas tree   to our friends.

4 We eat   roast turkey for dinner.

5 We sing carols   to open my presents.

Write the complete sentences here:

1 _____

2 _____

3 _____

4 _____

5 _____

Write the mixed-up words in the right order to make a sensible sentence.

1 The is name in of the Puss pantomime Boots.

_____

2 The Beanstalk of name and Jack is the pantomime the.

_____

_____

What's the same?

What's the same about gloves and mittens?

You wear them both on your hands.

 Write a sentence to answer each question.

1 What's the same about a hat and a cap?

_____

2 What's the same about shoes and slippers?

_____

Some words mean the **same** or almost the same as other words.

a <u>little</u> ant   a <u>tiny</u> ant

a <u>small</u> ant

 Join the words which have the **same** meaning.

big   tiny   end   ill

start   large   sick   stop

small   begin   halt   finish

 Complete each sentence.

1 Small means the same as _____ .

2 Another word for finish is _____ .

3 Someone who is ill is _____ .

4 Another word for large is _____ .

5 To start is to _____ .

6 To halt is to _____ .

What's different?

Some words mean the **opposite** of other words.

inside   outside

Join the words which have the **opposite** meanings.

push	cold	low	sweet
hot	long	happy	high
tiny	pull	sour	dirty
short	quick	clean	sad
slow	huge	shut	ugly
good	bad	pretty	open

Write the **opposite** of the word in the bracket in the space.

1 a _____ face (sad)

2 a _____ apple (good)

3 an _____ door (shut)

4 a _____ plate (clean)

5 a _____ orange (sour)

6 a _____ train (quick)

Complete each sentence with an **opposite**

1 Fire is hot, but ice is _____ .

2 A mouse is _____ , but an elephant is _____ .

3 A rabbit has a short neck, but a giraffe's neck is _____ .

4 A bungalow is a low building, but a tower is _____ .

5 A sheep is a tame animal, but a lion is _____ .

Which is it?

Do you write **is** or **are**?

is

This **is** a girl.

are

These **are** the children.

Always write **is** for **one** person or thing.
Always write **are** for **more than one**.

 Complete each sentence with **is** or **are**.

1 A robin _____ a bird.　**2** Robins _____ birds.

3 A bee _____ an insect.　**4** Bees _____ insects.

5 A tadpole _____ a young frog.　**6** Lambs _____ young sheep.

7 A baby horse _____ called a foal.　**8** Kittens _____ baby cats.

9 A cygnet _____ a young swan.　**10** Puppies _____ young dogs.

Do you write **is** or **his**?

his means: belonging to him

is

This **is** Tom's ball.

his

Tom kicked **his** ball.

 Complete each sentence with **is** or **his**.

1 Paul made a card for _____ sister.

2 Jane _____ coming to play today.

3 Susan _____ wearing her new coat.

4 Peter _____ eight years old, but _____ brother _____ only three.

5 Ben's aunt came to tea, but _____ uncle did not come because

he _____ at work.

Spelling

Some **double words** are made by joining two shorter words together like this:

 Join these short words together to make **double words**.

some	get	bath	fish
out	stairs	water	day
can	side	gold	fall
down	not	birth	board
for	thing	cup	room

 Complete these word sums to make **double words**.

1 snow + _____ = snowball

2 tea + _____ = teaspoon

3 _____ + hat = sunhat

4 book + shelf = _____

5 farm + _____ = farmhouse

6 _____ + bow = rainbow

7 arm + chair = _____

8 life + _____ = lifeboat

9 _____ + noon = afternoon

10 news + paper = _____

 Write the **same** missing word under each picture to make a **double word**.

fire _____   police _____   snow _____   milk _____

Action words

 Answer the questions by reading the chart.

	swim	fly	walk
cod	✓	✗	✗
dog	✓	✗	✓
owl	✗	✓	✓

1 What can walk and swim but not fly?

2 What can fly and walk but not swim?

 Draw a ring round the **action** word in each sentence.

1 Harry lost his coat.

2 Alan ate an orange.

3 Bob undid the knot.

4 Liam gave a present.

5 Jean heard the music.

 Write the **action** word in the puzzle.

1 l	o	s	t	
2				
3				
4				
5				

An **action** word is called a **verb**.

 Write the **verb** going down from 1-5.

— — — — —

Read this story:

Once there was a class of very noisy children. They laughed and shouted. They thumped and bumped. They even banged and whistled.

 Draw a ring round the things which the children did to make a noise. These are called **verbs**.

 Write the **verbs** here: _____ _____

_____ _____ _____ _____

Sentences

Read these sentences:

> Everyone enjoyed eating it.
>
> Mrs Cook made a cake.
>
> She put it in the oven to bake.

 Write the sentences under the pictures in the right order.

_____   _____   _____

_____   _____   _____

_____   _____   _____

Write each set of sentences in the right order.

He got on the bus. _____

He got off the bus. _____

Tom went to the bus stop. _____

Kim stuck a pin in it. _____

Pat blew up a balloon. _____

The balloon burst. _____

She fell to the ground. _____

Janvir climbed up a tree. _____

The branch snapped. _____

Right order

The days of the week are:

Friday	Tuesday	
Monday	Thursday	Wednesday
Sunday	Saturday	

Write the days of the week in the **right order**.

Start with Sunday.

1 _____ first

2 _____ second

3 _____ third

4 _____ fourth

5 _____ fifth

6 _____ sixth

7 _____ seventh

Complete these sentences:

1 Monday is the ___second___ day of the week.

2 The _____ day is Saturday.

3 Thursday is the _____ day.

4 The name of the _____ day is Tuesday.

5 Wednesday is the _____ day.

Write the number words in order of size starting with the smallest.

1 eight   six   two   _____ _____ _____

2 four   twelve   ten   _____ _____ _____

3 sixteen   twelve   fifteen   _____ _____ _____

4 thirteen   nine   three   _____ _____ _____

Is it true?

Which is the true sentence?

Scissors cut.   or   Scissors sing.

The true sentence is: Scissors cut.

Write the **true** sentence.

1   Fish swim in the sea.
    Fish swim on land.   _____

2   We go to bed to sleep.
    We go to bed to fly.   _____

3   The cook boiled an egg.
    The cook laid an egg.   _____

4   Snails move quickly.
    Snails move slowly.   _____

Draw a (ring) round the **right word** for each sentence.

                  tails.   glass.
1 Dogs have four ears.   2 I can see through   wood.
                  legs.   bricks.

                  water.   doors.
3 A car runs on   milk.   4 Houses have   horns.
                  petrol.   wheels.

                  feet.   toes.
5 We hear with our eyes.   6 Dentists care for our teeth.
                  ears.   fingers.

Information

The African elephant is the largest land animal. It can weigh 6 tonnes.

The giraffe is the tallest animal. It can grow to a height of 6 metres.

The cheetah is the fastest runner. It can move at 112 kilometres an hour.

The humming bird is the smallest bird. It can fit inside an egg-cup.

 Write the answers in the box.

1 Which animal is the tallest?

2 What is the name of the smallest bird?

3 What can an African elephant weigh?

4 How fast can a cheetah run?

Choose the correct word from the brackets and write the complete sentence.

1 The largest (sea, land) animal is the African elephant.

_____

2 The (shortest, tallest) of the animals is the giraffe.

_____

3 The humming bird can fit inside an (egg-cup, teapot).

_____

4 The fastest (swimmer, runner) of all the animals is a cheetah.

_____

Same and different

Look at the words round the sun.
Some of them mean the **same** as **bright**.

round   sweet
shiny   sparkling
little   dazzling

 Write the words which mean **bright** inside the sun.

 Draw a (ring) round the word which has the **same** meaning as the one in the box.

1 | small | smell   little   mouse   ant

2 | begin | end   bend   start   run

3 | plump | pig   lump   thin   fat

4 | fast | quick   last   key   door

5 | talk | stalk   speak   sleep   walk

 Write the words which mean the **opposite** of **hot** inside the snowman.

frosty   merry
white   cheerful
icy   cold

 Draw a (ring) round the word which has the **opposite** meaning to the one in the box.

1 | bad | bud   good   dog   bed

2 | dry | try   laugh   cry   wet

3 | old | new   you   gold   cold

4 | clean | white   nice   dirty   brown

5 | wrong | cross   right   sum   word

Thinking about nouns

| A **name** is the word by which something is known. | All words which are **names** are called **nouns**. | Ordinary names are called **common nouns**. |

Read all the words in the box.

 Draw a (ring) round each word which is a **common noun**.

| pencil | chair | open | eat | spade |
| write | sit | door | cake | dig |

 Write the 5 **common nouns** here:

_____ _____ _____ _____ _____

 Write <u>one</u> of the 5 **common nouns** in each sentence.

1 I can sit on a _____ .

2 A gardener can dig with a _____ .

3 My dog can open the _____ with his paw.

4 I like a sharp _____ when I write.

5 I could eat a big, cream _____ .

What can you eat?

Pull the **nouns** apart.

 Write the 5 **common nouns**.

eggjambunpiechips

26

Thinking about verbs

Action words tell us what is **being done** in a sentence.	Action words are called **verbs**.

Read all the words in the box.

 Draw a (ring) round each word which is a **verb**.

pencil	chair	open	eat	spade
write	sit	door	cake	dig

 Write the 5 **verbs** here:

_____   _____   _____   _____   _____

 Write <u>one</u> of the **verbs** in each sentence.

1 I can _____ on a chair.

2 A gardener can _____ with a spade.

3 My dog can _____ the door with his paw.

4 I like a sharp pencil when I _____ .

5 I could _____ a big, cream cake.

What can you do?

Pull the **verbs** apart.

Write the 5 **verbs**.

runwalkskiphopswim

Spelling

Two sounds can be pushed together to make **one** sound like this:

 Write **two** letters which sound together to complete each word.

_ _ r e e   _ _ e e l   _ _ a i r   _ _ i p   _ _ e r r y   _ _ i r t y

Here are more sounds which can be pushed together:

d r   b l   f l   c l   c r   f r

 Write **two** letters which sound together to complete each word.

_ _ o g   _ _ o c k   _ _ o w n   _ _ u m   _ _ u e   _ _ a g

 Write the answer in the sentence and in the puzzle, using the words you have made.

1 _____ is the name of a colour.

2 A _____ tells the time.

3 A _____ has big feet.

4 A _____ can be used to give a signal.

5 You can beat a _____ .

6 A tadpole is a young _____ .

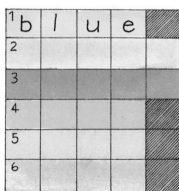

True or not true

Study each of these flags.

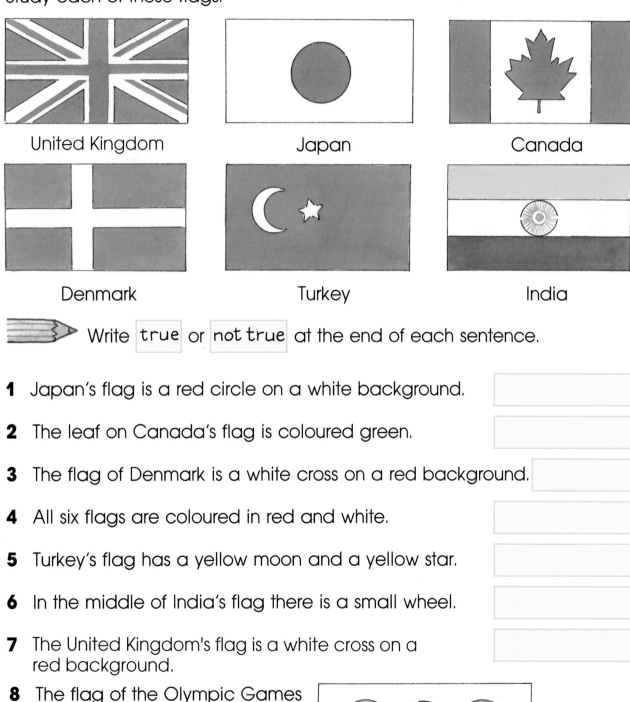

United Kingdom   Japan   Canada

Denmark   Turkey   India

Write | true | or | not true | at the end of each sentence.

1 Japan's flag is a red circle on a white background.

2 The leaf on Canada's flag is coloured green.

3 The flag of Denmark is a white cross on a red background.

4 All six flags are coloured in red and white.

5 Turkey's flag has a yellow moon and a yellow star.

6 In the middle of India's flag there is a small wheel.

7 The United Kingdom's flag is a white cross on a
red background.

8 The flag of the Olympic Games
has five rings.

Rhymes

Words which have the same sounds at the ends are called **rhymes**.

Make **pairs of rhymes** from the words in the box like this:

leg	ship	back
see	coat	sing
wing	trip	boat
wag	sack	bag
me	beg	

In each line write 4 more words which **rhyme** with the word in the box like this:

Jan   c a n   m a n   r a n   p a n

bat	c _ _	f _ _	s _ _	p _ _
get	w _ _	l _ _	m _ _	s _ _
pin	b _ _	w _ _	t _ _	f _ _
hot	p _ _	c _ _	r _ _	l _ _
mug	b _ _	r _ _	h _ _	t _ _

Finish each of the following with a rhyming word:

1 Hark! Hark!
The dogs do _____.

2 Rain, Rain! Go away,
Come again another _____.

3 Twinkle, twinkle little _____
How I wonder what you are!

4 Riddle me! Riddle me! What is that:
Over your head and under your
_____ ?

Memorizing

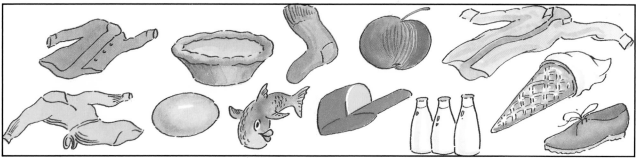

Say the names of the 12 things in the picture.
When you are ready, cover the picture.

Draw or write all the things you can remember in each set.

**things
you can
wear**

**things
you can
eat**

Write how many you remembered.

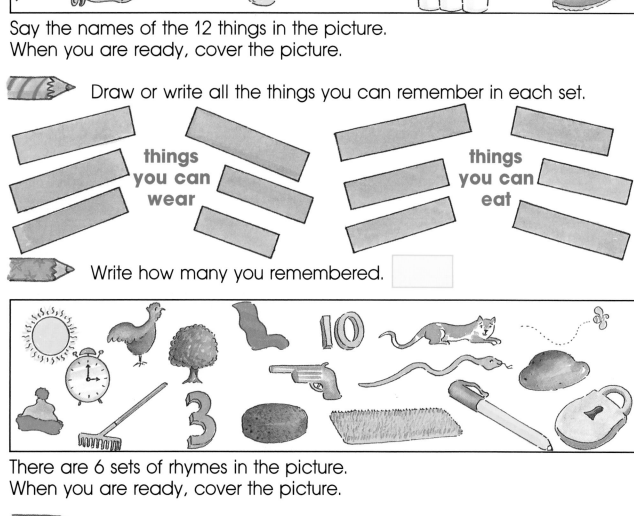

There are 6 sets of rhymes in the picture.
When you are ready, cover the picture.

Write all the things you can remember in rhyme sets.

sun				
gun				
bun				

Write how many you remembered.

Answers

To Parents: We have not provided *all* the answers here. We suggest that items to be drawn on clocks, snakes, etc., should be checked by you. In the case of activities where calculations are performed by your child, it would be good practice to get him/her to use a calculator to check the answers.

Answers to alphabet questions on pp 2, 5, 7 and 9 can be checked from the alphabet on p2.

P2

2 arm	leg	toe
3 coat	hat	shoe
4 Carol	Janet	Tom
5 den	sty	zoo
6 cat	dog	pig

P3

2 fruits
3 vegetables

2 These are all clothes.
3 These are all insects.

P4

The puppet...
Once there...
The King...
By morning...

P5

1 a,e,i,o or u   2 a, e, i, o or u
3 i, o or u   4 a, i or o
5 a, e, i or u   6 a, i, o or u

by cry my try fly sty dry why

1 fly, by   2 try
3 dry   4 my
5 sty   6 why, cry

P6

A mighty lion...
The lion agreed...
Some time later...
The mouse...

1 paw
2 go free
3 trapped, net
4 mouse, ropes, lion

P7

an egg **a** hat **a** tree
an umbrella
a ball **an** owl **an** arm
an island **a** flower
a man

an old hat **a** pretty picture
an angry face **a** new coat
an ugly duckling **a** happy teacher

1 two   4 two, to
2 to   5 two, to
3 to

P8

1 Diana and her friends were playing rounders.
2 Robert enjoys playing football.
3 Lucy went to see her grandmother.
4 Sharks and whales swim in water.
5 Birds and aeroplanes fly in the air.
6 Most apes and monkeys live in trees.

P9

2 fin   4 beg
3 sty   5 not

P10

1 pig
2 bed   5 wet
3 man   6 sun
4 cot

P10 (continued)

1 **sp**ider   5 fi**sh**/**st**
2 **sh**ip   6 wa**sp**/**sh**
3 **st**ick   7 br**ush**
4 **sw**im   8 ne**st**

1 spell   3 Sharks
2 sweets   4 swing

P11

2 triangle
3 week
4 girl
5 plate

Dictionary

P12

1 Monday
2 3 + 3
3 December 25th
4 Twenty-six
5 Uncle

1 Which dog keeps the best time?
2 Which animal goes to bed with its shoes on?
3 When is it bad luck to be followed by a black cat?

P13

1 Birds of the Air
2 Fish of the Sea
3 Farm Animals
4 Fish of the Sea
5 Birds of the Air

1 4   4 9
2 20   5 26
3 14

puppy   kitten   duckling

P14

slipper   sandal   shoe

ball	rose	slipper
doll	poppy	sandal
jigsaw	lily	shoe

chimney	brake
window	door
stairs	wiper
knocker	tyres
walls	horn
gutter	wheel
door	window

apple ink eel owl umbrella

P15

2 a pack of sweets
3 a book of puzzles
4 a pair of slippers
5 a box of cards

1 ...I wake up early.
2 ...to open my presents.
3 ...shines with fairy lights.
4 ...roast turkey for dinner.
5 ...to our friends.

1 Puss in Boots is the name of the pantomime.
2 Jack and the Beanstalk is the name of the pantomime.

P16

1 You wear them both on your head.
2 You wear them both on your feet.

start	begin
small	tiny
end	finish
sick	ill
halt	stop

P17

hot	cold	low	high
tiny	huge	happy	sad
short	long	sour	sweet
slow	quick	clean	dirty
good	bad	shut	open
		pretty	ugly

1 happy   4 dirty
2 bad   5 sweet
3 open   6 slow

1 cold   4 high
2 small, big   5 wild
3 long

P18

1, 3, 5, 7, 9: is
2, 4, 6, 8, 10: are

1 his   4 is, his, is
2 is   5 his, is
3 is

P19

outside	bathroom
cannot	waterfall
downstairs	goldfish
forget	birthday
	cupboard

1 ball   6 rain
2 spoon   7 armchair
3 sun   8 boat
4 bookshelf   9 after
5 house   10 newspaper

fire**man**   snow**man**
police**man**   milk**man**

P20

1 dog   2 owl

2 ate
3 undid
4 gave
5 heard

laugh

laughed, shouted, thumped, bumped, banged, whistled

P21

Mrs Cook...
She put...
Everyone...

Tom went...
He got on...
He got off...

Pat blew...
Kim stuck...
The balloon...

Janvir...
The branch...
She fell...

P22

2 seventh   4 third
3 fifth   5 fourth

1 two, six, eight
2 four, ten, twelve
3 twelve, fifteen, sixteen
4 three, nine, thirteen

P23

1 Fish swim in the sea.
2 We go to bed to sleep.
3 The cook boiled an egg.
4 Snails move slowly.

1 legs   2 glass
3 petrol   4 doors
5 ears   6 teeth

P24

1 giraffe   3 6 tonnes
2 humming bird   4 112 kilometres an hour

1 land   3 egg-cup
2 tallest   4 runner

P25

sparkling, dazzling, shiny

1 little   4 quick
2 start   5 speak
3 fat

icy, frosty, cold

1 good   4 dirty
2 wet   5 right
3 new

P26

pencil, chair, spade, door, cake

1 chair   4 pencil
2 spade   5 cake
3 door

egg, jam, bun, pie, chips

P27

open, eat, write, sit, dig

1 sit   4 write
2 dig   5 eat
3 open

run, walk, skip, hop, swim

P28

th, wh, ch, wh, ch, th

fr, cl, cl, dr, bl, fl

2 clock   5 drum
3 clown   6 frog
4 flag

P29

1 true   5 not true
2 not true   6 true
3 true   7 not true
4 not true   8 true

P30

leg, beg   ship, trip
wing, sing   coat, boat
wag, bag   sack, back

cat, fat, sat, pat
wet, let, met, set
bin, win, tin, fin
pot, cot, rot, lot

bug, rug, hug, tug

1 bark   2 day
3 star   4 hat

P31

coat	cap	tart	apple
dress	shirt	fish	milk
sock	shoe	egg	ice-cream

hen	clock	hat	tree	rake
ten, 10	sock	mat	three, 3	cake
pen	lock	cat	bee	snake